Garfield

Just Good Friends

JIM DAVIS

Ravette London

This edition first published by
Ravette Limited 1987

Printed and bound in Great Britain
for Ravette Limited,
3 Glenside Estate, Star Road, Partridge Green,
Horsham, Sussex RH13 8RA
by Cox & Wyman Ltd, Reading

ISBN 0 948456 68 X

ODIE ISN'T EXACTLY THE BRIGHTEST DOG AROUND

HIS I.Q. IS SO LOW, YOU CAN'T TEST IT. YOU HAVE TO DIG FOR IT

© 1986 United Feature Syndicate, Inc.

JIM DAVIS 12-5

© 1986 United Feature Syndicate, Inc.

REMEMBER, GARFIELD, THERE IS NO GREATER FAILING THAN APATHY

© 1986 United Feature Syndicate, Inc.

SO WHAT?

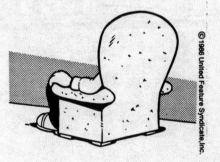

© 1986 United Feature Syndicate, Inc.

© 1986 United Feature Syndicate, Inc.

JIM DAVIS 8-28

© 1986 United Feature Syndicate, Inc.

THIS HAS POSSIBILITIES

THUD

JIM DAVIS 10-6

© 1986 United Feature Syndicate, Inc.

DRIVE-THRU RESTAURANTS ARE SO CONVENIENT

BLAM!

© 1986 United Feature Syndicate, Inc.

JIM DAVIS 10-9

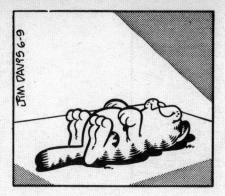

GARFIELD!

© 1986 United Feature Syndicate, Inc.

5-7

WHAT DID YOU DO TO MY FERN?!

I (BURP) PRUNED IT

JIM DAVIS

5-10

© 1986 United Feature Syndicate, Inc.

CRASH!

WHAT MADE YOU DO THAT?

MY SENSE OF AESTHETICS

JIM DAVIS

© 1986 United Feature Syndicate, Inc.

WHIP! WHIP! WHIP!

OTHER GARFIELD BOOKS IN THIS SERIES

LANDSCAPE SERIES

TV SPECIALS

Here Comes Garfield	£2.95
Garfield On The Town	£2.95
Garfield In The Rough	£2.95
Garfield In Disguise	£2.95
Garfield In Paradise	£2.95

All these books are available at your local bookshop or newsagent, or can be ordered direct from the publisher. Just tick the titles you require and fill in the form below. Prices and availability subject to change without notice.

Ravette Limited, 3 Glenside Estate, Star Road, Partridge Green, Horsham, West Sussex RH13 8RA

Please send a cheque or postal order, and allow the following for postage and packing. UK: Pocket books and TV Specials — 45p for one book plus 20p for the second book and 15p for each additional book. Landscape Series — 45p for one book plus 30p for each additional book.

Name ....

Address ....

....